The *12 Bar Blues Bible*

for Piano/Keyboards

By Andrew D. Gordon

Styles include:

Blues, Boogie-Woogie, Rock, Gospel

Funky-Blues, Jazz-Blues

isbn 1-882146-58-1

Front cover illustration: Jim Stubbington

Published & Distributed exclusively by A.D.G. Productions
15517 Cordary Ave., Lawndale CA 90260
web site address http://www.adgproductions.com
e mail adgordon@adgproductions.com
copyright © 1997, 2003 A.D.G. Productions

CONTENTS

Preface

Thank you for buying this book. Due to the overwhelming demand of my book *"100 Ultimate Blues Riffs"*, I decided to author another book solely on blues piano/keyboard playing. Most Blues tunes are made up of a 12 bar progression and I thought that a book that show the various types and styles of 12 bar blues progressions would be useful to musicians and students.

The book includes over 50 examples that cover a range of *styles*, (**blues, jazz-blues, minor-blues, funky-blues, country-blues, rock-blues, latin-blues, gospel-blues**), *tempos, rhythms and key signatures*. There is a brief description, followed by each of the examples perfectly notated, along with the chord symbols. The latter part of the book contains a chapter on the **"Basics Of Blues Improvisation"** for anyone who is just starting out in the world of improvising using the Blues as a starting point.

The audio CD that comes with the book has all the examples recorded with the piano left hand part on the left channel and the piano right hand part on the right channel along with a drum track in stereo. This format enables you to, by turning the balance control to the left, hear the left hand being played so that you can practice the right hand part along with it and vice versa.

Jam - A - Long Tracks

At the end of the CD there are seven **jam - along tracks,** each about *three minutes in length* so that you may try out examples in the book or your own improvisational ideas along with a rhythm section of **organ, bass & drums**.

Notice To Computer and Sequencer Users

This program comes with an optional MIDI file disk and loads into your sequencing software by selecting **"Load MIDI file",** please refer to your manual for further instructions. Load in the example you want to listen to or practice. Track 1 is the right hand piano part, Track 2 is the left hand piano part, both on MIDI channel 1, Track 3 is the drum track on MIDI channel 10.

The MIDI file disks are formatted for **IBM** or **Macintosh** computers as well as **General MIDI** keyboards and sequencers with disk drives. If you bought this product without the MIDI disk and would like to purchase the MIDI disk separately or have any compatibility questions please contact us at: (310) 379 1568

A Brief Description Of Each Riff

Riff 1

This uptempo boogie woogie progression in the key of C starts with a pick up by the right hand. The left hand plays a common boogie woogie bass pattern while the right hand plays a repetitive melodic pattern. As with any boogie woogie style bass line make sure the left hand propels the music forward by having steady time. The right hand will then fit in comfortably with the left hand.

Riff 2

This slow blues in the key of Eb has a bass line that uses the 1st., 3rd., 5th. & 6th. notes of the scale. This example goes to the Ab7 (IV) chord in the second measure instead of staying on the I chord. I tried to make the melody simple but melodic.

Riff 3

This funky blues in the key of Bb uses a common bass line that includes playing notes octaves apart. The right hand plays a rhythmic keyboard style, great to use if you are a keyboardist in a blues band. If the octave stretch in the right hand is a little tough then leave out the bottom note of the chord.

Riff 4

This medium tempo boogie woogie piece has a very happy sound to it and I was inspired to write it from the time when I first learnt to play this style back in the late 1960's. The chord progression is not the typical I, IV, V sequence but has a jazzier flavor to it with the use of a II V I progression in measures 2 to 3 and 9 to 11. Once again the left hand has a strong rhythmic accompaniment.

Riff 5

This example has a bass line that is a variation on the previous boogie woogie bass lines. Notice the chromatic rundown with the right hand in measures 9 and 10 on the second beat of each of the two measures. This chromatic (half step) rundown is a common device used in both blues & jazz.

Riff 6

This repetitive rock blues riff is played by both hands in unison. Once again, the use of octaves are used as part of the riff. This example is often used by guitar players but can be played by keyboard players either by itself or in conjunction with the guitar player. Notice that there are no 3^{rds}., in this example. A lot of guitar based blues & rock leave out the thirds giving the music an ambiguous sound because the chord is neither major or minor.

Riff 7

This uptempo rock blues example gets close to rock & roll and has the right hand playing in a rhythmic style along with one measure fills as in measures 4 and 12. The left hand is playing a repetitive straight eighth note pattern.

Riff 8

In this medium tempo boogie woogie example, the left and right hands are playing similar patterns with the right hand playing a little more harmonically. The bass riff is the same as in example 5. Notice that both the right & left hands are played in the bass clef.

Riff 9

This mid tempo rock/gospel blues example has a much different feel than the previous examples. This example is in a minor key (A minor) and the use of octaves in measures 9 & 10 give a distinct gospel sound. Quite often in minor blues progressions the #V chord (F7) is used one measure before the V (E7) chord as the progression descends back to the I (Am) chord.

Riff 10

This example uses a "Wurlitzer" piano sound commonly used in the 1960's and early 1970's before the Fender Rhodes became popular. It has a grittier sound than the Fender Rhodes and Ray Charles was one of the first pianists to incorporate the "Wurlitzer" piano sound. This example is reminiscent of the mid to late 1960's British pop sound, such as the Beatles, who used a lot of blues influences in their music.

Riff 11

This is another example that is more pop orientated than straight ahead blues. I used a "Fender Rhodes" sound so that you could hear the differences between the "Wurlitzer" and the "Fender Rhodes" in this and the previous example. Measures 11 and 12 consists of the right hand playing the blues scale (see section on basic blues improvisation at the back of the book for further information). The pattern is 5 notes long (G, C#, C, Bb & G) so that each note is placed on a different beat of the measure each time it is played giving a subtle off time feel.

Riff 12

This example has a nice swinging boogie woogie feel to it. The left hand is playing a two measure boogie woogie phrase while the right hand is playing a rhythmic keyboard style that is anticipating the first beat of the measure as in measures 3, 5, 7, 9 or laying back off the beat as in measures 2, 6,10, 12.

Riff 13

This example is a much used blues/rock progression in a minor key (Ebm). Notice how the octave bass is stationary while the chords move. For instance while the bass is playing an octave Eb the chords are moving from Ebm to Gb (a minor third up from Eb) and then to Ab (a fourth up from Eb). The same progression occurs when the chord changes to Abm in measures 5 & 6 . To finally resolve back to the Ebm the chords ascend from Cb (measure 9) through Db (measure 10) to Ebm. The chords are often played on the off beat.

Riff 14

This somewhat simple funky blues pattern harks back to the early 1960's with such songs as "Mustang Sally", Notice, once again, the anticipation of the first beat of the measure by playing the notes on the last eighth note of the measure instead of the first beat of the next measure giving the rhythm a push. Notice the eighth note staccato rhythm on the V chord (F7) in measure 12, a common device used by James Brown to bring the song back to the I chord (Bb) again.

Riff 15

This example does not go through the normal 12 bar blues progression. It starts on the IV chord (C7) instead of normally starting on the I chord (G7). However, there is still the V (D7) to IV (C7) to I chord (G7) descending chord pattern at the end of the sequence.

Riff 16
This funky blues example in the key of B is adapted to keyboards from a guitar riff taken from a Junior Wells song. Make sure when playing the four 16th. notes in the third beat of each measure that you alternate between the 2nd. & 3rd. fingers. Trying to play all four notes with one finger is much more difficult.

Riff 17
This mid tempo rock/blues example in the key of C contains two commonly used devices for blues keyboard playing. The use of grace notes such as in measures 1, 2, 3 etc. where the grace note is generally the #4 of the chord (F# in measure 1) or the b3 of the chord (Eb in measure 2) giving a characteristic blues sound. The second device is the use of triplets over a straight rock beat as in measure 9. The left hand is playing a driving eighth note pattern.

Riff 18
This example contains an 8 measure progression instead of the normal 12 bar blues. I included it all the same just to give a little variety to the chord progressions. The use of tremolos as in measure 5 is another important feature of playing blues piano. The first two beats of each of the first four measures of the piece is identical while the last two beats contain different fills another common practice of blues playing. This refers to the use of repetitive riffs followed by improvisational fills. Try this out for yourself by playing the first two beats as written and then creating your own fills on the last two beats.

Riff 19
This mid tempo funky blues example uses the dominant7#9 chord effectively. Notice in measure 4 how there is a slide up to the G7 chord from a half step below (A# C# E to B D F) another useful tool in blues & jazz.

Riff 20
This example has a Latin flavor to it with the bass, playing a typical Latin bass part. I would strongly recommend as with all the other examples to practice each hand separately before trying to put both hands together. There is a great deal of syncopation between the two hands and each hand needs to be practiced individually. If you enjoyed this particular example and want to find out more about Salsa or Latin piano styles I would thoroughly recommend a book by Carlos Campos called "Salsa & Afro Cuban Montunos for Piano" a book we publish.

Riff 21
This boogie woogie piece consists of a bass line that is playing octaves using the 1, 3, 5 & 6 notes of the chord. Once again grace notes and triplet figures are used to produce an authentic blues sound.

Riff 22
This is another example of a medium tempo boogie woogie piece and comments made to previous boogie woogie pieces apply to this one as well.

Riff 23
This example as with previous boogie woogie examples consist of very strong & rhythmical bass lines. There are many different bass patterns that can be used either separately or interchangeably. Try and learn and memorize as many of these examples as possible.

Riff 24

This gospel inspired 16 measure blues in the key of Gm is played in ¾ time. Full chords as well as octaves gives this example that gospel sound. Refer to my book "Gospel Riffs God Would Love to Hear" for an in depth look at gospel piano/keyboard playing.

Riff 25

This medium tempo funky blues uses a repetitive riff that incorporates both hands playing a syncopated pattern. Notice that both staves are written in the bass clef.. Because of the very syncopated rhythm practice this example at a very slow tempo counting the rhythm very strictly. This type of piano/keyboard playing was very popular in the late 1960's and 1970's with the use of the "Clavinet" a very percussive keyboard instrument. Keyboard players such as: Stevie Wonder, Herbie Hancock and Billy Preston perfected this style.

Riff 26

This boogie woogie example in the key of D uses a dense 3 note chord pattern with the left hand. Notice the typical blues ending in measures 11 and 12.

Riff 27

This is another Latin influenced blues piece in the key of Am. The bass line is playing a 1 - 5 - octave pattern while the right hand is playing a mixture of chords, octaves and single note melody lines.

Riff 28

This medium tempo jazz swing blues distinguishes itself from the normal 12 bar blues progression because of the more sophisticated chord sequence that is used. Measures 7 & 8 consist of a chromatic run down (C7, B7, Bb7 & A7) which then proceed to a II V I (Dm7 G7 C7) chord progression in measures 9 through 11. This is followed by a popular I VI II V (C7 A7 Dm7 G7) turnaround in measures 11 & 12. The left hand is playing a walking bass line typically used in jazz.

Riff 29

This funky blues example uses 9th. chords, played rhythmically with the right hand, throughout the piece while the left hand is playing a syncopated bass line. Instead of staying on the C9 chord for the first four measures, there are two passing chords Eb9 & D9 at the end of each measure to make the progression more interesting.

Riff 30

This example uses another boogie woogie bass pattern. The right hand is playing rhythmic patterns using 6th. chords. The notes in the first beat of the first measure consists of A, C# F# (the F# being the sixth note in the scale of A). The same applies when the chords change to D and E. The 6th. and 9th. chords generally give the blues a more jazzier feel.

Riff 31

This rock/blues example uses the "Bo Diddley" beat, a beat that "Bo Diddley created in the early 1960's and which has been used in countless rock & blues songs. Notice the vamping back and forth of the chords such as: Ab to Gb back to Ab. The bass is once again playing a syncopated line with octave run ups at the end of each measure.

Riff 32

This uptempo minor jazz blues example, once again, utilizes a walking bass line through the progression. Two jazz songs come to mind that use this progression are "Sugar" and "Blue Bossa".

Riff 33

This funky blues example in the key of F alternates between the I (F) and the IV (Bb) chord in each of the I, IV (Bb to Eb a fourth above Bb) & V (C to F a fourth above C) positions. The bass is playing a repetitive figure using the b3 to the natural 3 of the chord.

Riff 34

Another mid tempo funky blues this time in the key of A, not a favorite key for keyboard players but definitely a favorite for guitar players. With that in mind it is important to try these riffs out in as many keys as possible especially if you are going to be playing with other musicians. A singer may not have the range to play in a key that you are accustomed to playing and therefore you will have to play in a key that suits them.

Riff 35

This straight ahead blues piece in a minor key has the left hand playing octaves. In measures 9 and 10 the right hand is playing the chords of D and C but without the 3rd. giving, as explained in a previous example, an ambiguous sound neither major or minor. This particular chord without the third is used by many rock & blues guitarists.

Riff 36 .

Another boogie woogie piece, nothing more to add that has been mentioned in previous examples.

Riff 37

This funky blues in the key of E incorporates the dominant7#9 chord. I used a "Wurlitzer" piano sound to produce attacking & gritty sound that the "Wurlitzer" is famous for.

Riff 38

This funky blues piece in the key of B minor uses the Rhodes sound to produce a jazzy flavor. Most of the melody line is based on the B blues scale however in measure 9 the melody line is based on the G blues scale played over the G9 chord.

Riff 39

Another boogie woogie piece with the left hand playing an octave bass line while the right hand is playing a rhythmic pattern.

Riff 40

This slow minor blues, again using a Rhodes sound to produce a jazzy flavor, incorporates the use of minor 10th.s with the left hand. The minor 10th.s may be a stretch for some people and if that is the case play the octave of the chord rather than the 10th. (Play D - A - D) instead of (D - A - F).The minor 10th. position is immediately followed in the measure by the minor 9th. giving a rhythmic pulse to the piece. The right hand is playing tasteful melodic lines that are very bluesy finally resolving in a Dm(maj7) chord, a popular ending chord.

Riff 41

I thought I would add a couple of country blues examples in the "mix". This example in the key of E utilizes a typical country bass line using the 1 - 5 - octave of each chord. Notice in measure 4 there is a chromatic octave run up from the E chord to the A chord in measure 5. Country is generally not as syncopated as blues, funk or jazz and does not often use the blues scale. It does, however, use chromatic runs as shown in measures 9 & 10.

Riff 42

This country blues riff consists of the left hand playing 1 - 3 - 5 of the chord. Chromatic runs occur in measures 7 & 8.

Riff 43

This slow blues uses triplet rhythms and very fast repetitive runs, using the blues scale, to produce tension in the music. The left hand is playing a bass line using octaves.

Riff 44

This slow blues features the use of tremolos in measures 1, 2, 3 & 9. Use your 2nd. & 4th. fingers to play the tremolos. Again, there are fast blues scale runs while the left hand is playing a bass line using octaves.

Riff 45

A boogie woogie riff that uses the same characteristics as previous boogie woogie riffs.

Riff 46

This rock/blues example consists of the left hand playing the octave of the chord on the 1st. and 3rd. beats with the actual chord played on the 2nd. & 4th. beats. The right hand is generally playing octaves around the A blues scale. I particularly like measure 6 where the chord changes from Am7 to A7 and how the melody follows the chord progression. Notice the descending chord progression in measures 8 & 9 from Dm7 - Dm(maj7) - Dm7 - Dm6.

Riff 47

This uptempo jazz blues example again uses a walking bass line as a foundation for the piece. The chord progression or harmony is the most complex of any of the examples in this book and moves around the cycle of fifths using II - V - I progressions such as Am7 - D7 - Gm7, Fm7 - Bb7 - Ebmaj7, Dm7 - G7 - Cm7.

Riff 48

This gospel/blues example uses the "wurlitzer" piano sound to produce an uplifting feel. The left hand is playing a very syncopated bass line while the right hand is playing a mixture of rhythmic chords, single note lines and octaves.

Riff 49

This funky blues with a Latin feel consists of a syncopated bass line that really stands out. The right hand is generally playing melodic lines using the Ab blues scale along with the 6th. & 9th. notes of the Ab major scale. In measure 11 there is a chromatic run up using notes a 4th. apart.

Riff 50

This example as well as riff 51 has a modern hip hop feel to it. Once again the use of the C blues scale is prevalent throughout the piece.

Riff 51

This example starts and finishes with a chromatic melodic line. The left hand, instead of playing a bass line as in the previous example, is playing chords. It starts off with whole notes and then builds up into more complex rhythms.

RIFF 1

Boogie Woogie Blues

Composed & Arranged by
Andrew D. Gordon

CD track 1

♩ = 160

RIFF 2

Slow Blues

Composed & Arranged by
Andrew D. Gordon

CD track 2

♩ = 75

RIFF 3

Funky Blues

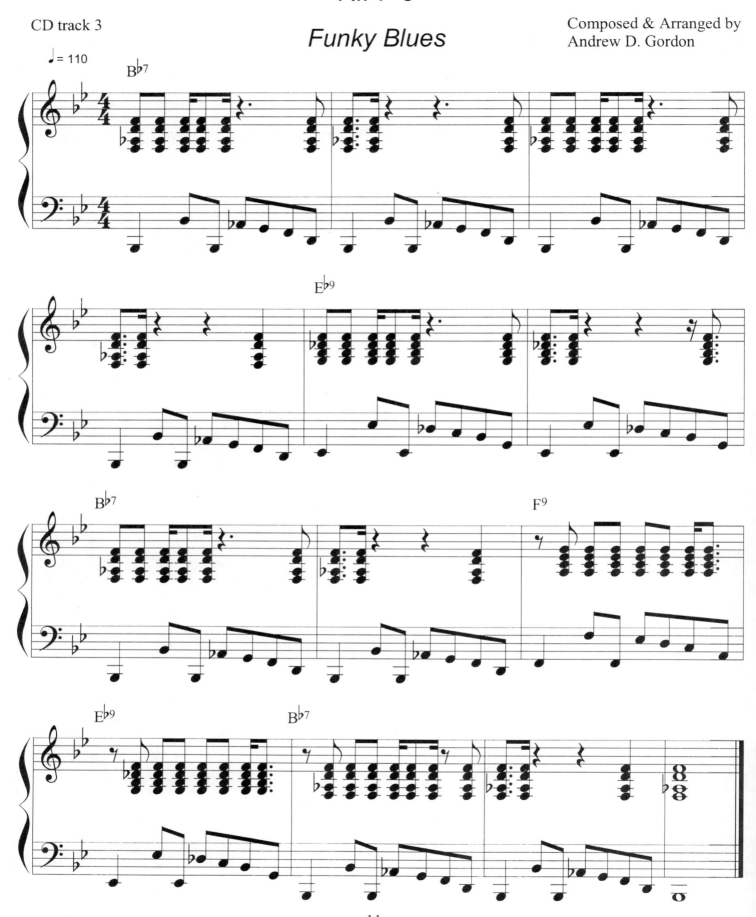

CD track 3

Composed & Arranged by
Andrew D. Gordon

11

RIFF 4
Boogie Woogie Blues

CD track 4

♩ = 95

Composed & Arranged by
Andrew D. Gordon

RIFF 5

Boogie Woogie Blues

Composed & Arranged by
Andrew D. Gordon

CD track 5

♩ = 95

RIFF 6

Mid Tempo Blues

Composed & Arranged by
Andrew D. Gordon

RIFF 7

Composed & Arranged by
Andrew D. Gordon

Rock Blues

CD track 7

♩ = 180

15

RIFF 8

Boogie Woogie Blues

Composed & Arranged by
Andrew D. Gordon

♩ = 110

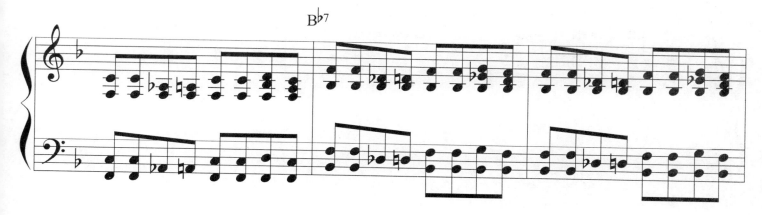

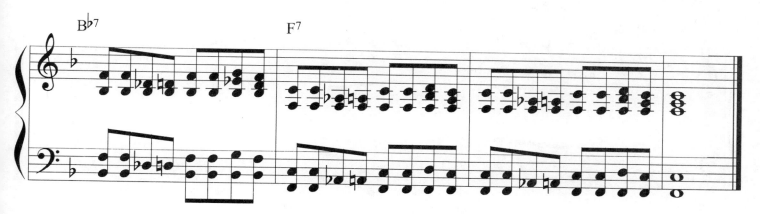

RIFF 9

Rock Gospel Blues

Composed & Arranged by
Andrew D. Gordon

17

RIFF 10

Rock Blues

Composed & Arranged by
Andrew D. Gordon

♩ = 115

18

RIFF 11

Rock Blues

Composed & Arranged by
Adnrew D. Gordon

♩ = 130

RIFF 12

CD track 12

♩ = 120

Boogie Woogie Blues

Composed & Arranged by
Andrew D. Gordon

RIFF 13

Rock Blues

Composed & Arranged by
Andrew D. Gordon

CD track 13

RIFF 14

Funky Blues

CD track 14

Composed & Arranged by
Andrew D. Gordon

RIFF 15

CD track 15

Mid Tempo Blues

Composed & Arranged by
Andrew D. Gordon

♩ = 120

23

RIFF 16

Funky Blues

CD track 16

Composed & Arranged by
Andrew D. Gordon

RIFF 17

Rock Blues

Composed & Arranged by
Andrew D. Gordon

♩ = 120

RIFF 18

Rock Blues

CD track 18

Composed & Arranged by
Andrew D. Gordon

RIFF 19

Funky Blues

Composed & Arranged by
Andrew D. Gordon

RIFF 20

Latin Blues

Composed & Arranged by
Andrew D. Gordon

RIFF 21

Boogie Woogie Blues

Composed & Arranged by
Andrew D. Gordon

♩= 110

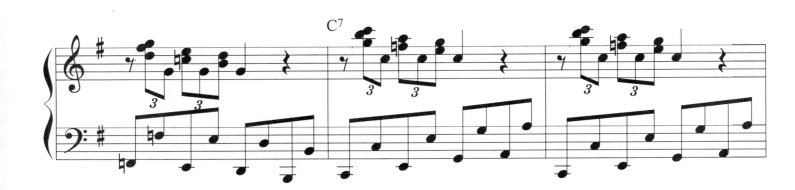

29

RIFF 22

Boogie Woogie Blues

CD track 22

Composed & Arranged by
Andrew D. Gordon

♩ = 107

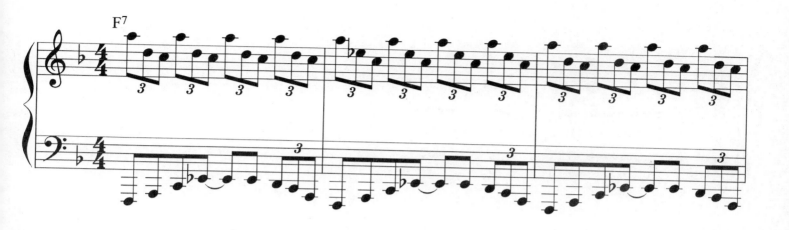

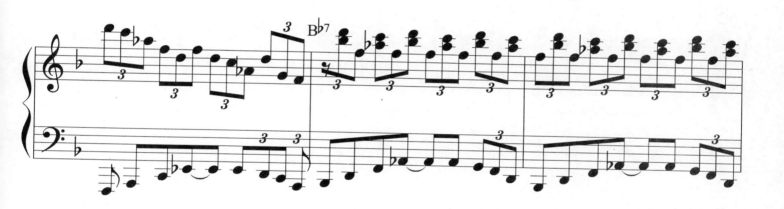

RIFF 23

Boogie Woogie Blues

CD track 23

♩ = 100

Composed & Arranged by
Andrew D. Gordon

RIFF 24

16 bar Gospel Blues 3/4 time

Composed &Arranged by
Andrew D. Gordon

33

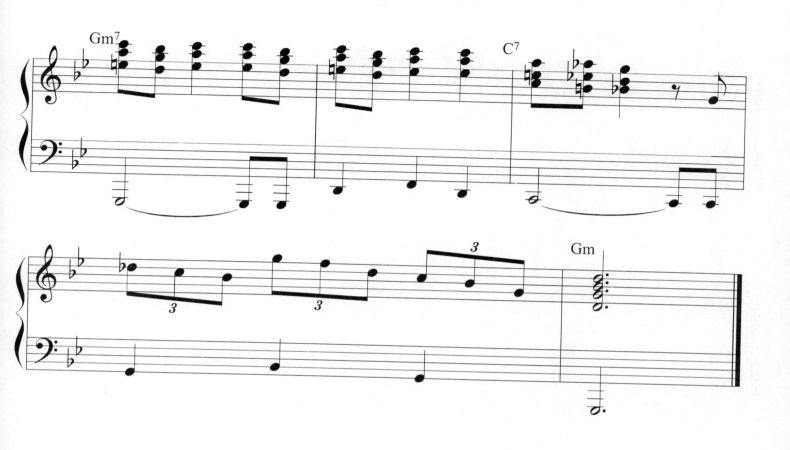

RIFF 25

Funky Blues

CD track 25

Composed & Arranged by
Andrew D. Gordon

RIFF 26

Boogie Woogie Blues

CD track 26

♩ = 100

Composed & Arranged by
Andrew D. Gordon

36

RIFF 27

Latin Blues

CD track 27

Composed & Arranged by
Andrew D. Gordon

RIFF 28

Jazz Blues

Composed & Arranged by
Andrew D. Gordon

RIFF29

Funky Blues

Composed & Arranged by
Andrew D. Gordon

CD track 29

RIFF 30

Boogie Woogie Blues

CD track 30

♩ = 80

Composed & Arranged by
Andrew D. Gordon

40

RIFF 31

Rock Blues

Composed & Arranged by
Andrew D. Gordon

CD track 31

♩ = 95

41

RIFF 32

Minor Jazz Blues

CD track 32

Compsed & Arranged by
Andrew D. Gordon

RIFF 33

Funky Blues

Composed & Arranged by
Andrew D. Gordon

RIFF 34

Funky Blues

CD track 34

Composed & Arranged by
Andrew D. Gordon

RIFF 35

Minor Blues

CD track 35

Composed & Arranged by
Andrew D. Gordon

RIFF 36

Boogie Woogie Blues

Composed & Arranged by
Andrew D. Gordon

CD track 36

♩ = 110

RIFF 37

Funky Blues

Composed & Arranged by
Andrew D. Gordon

CD track 37

♩ = 85

RIFF 38

Funky Blues

CD track 38

Composed & Arranged by
Andrew D. Gordon

RIFF 39

Boogie Woogie Blues

CD track 39

Composed & Arranged by
Andrew D. Gordon

RIFF 40

Slow Minor Blues

Composed & Arranged by
Andrew D. Gordon

RIFF 41

Country Blues

Composed & Arranged by
Andrew D. Gordon

CD track 41

♩ = 165

RIFF 42

Country Blues

Composed & Arranged by
Andrew D. Gordon

RIFF 43

Slow Blues

CD track 43

Composed & Arranged by
Andrew D. Gordon

♩ = 70

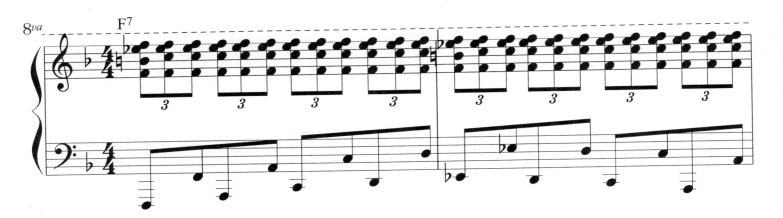

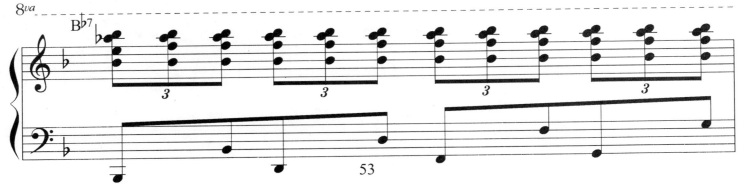

53

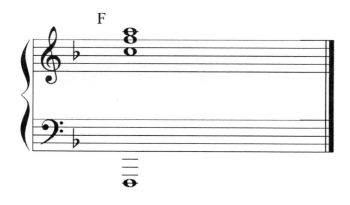

RIFF 44

Slow Blues

Composed & Arranged by
Andrew D. Gordon

CD track 44

♩ = 60

RIFF 45

Boogie Woogie Blues

Composed & Arranged by
Andrew D. Gordon

CD track 45

♩ = 180

58

RIFF 46

Rock Blues

Composed & Arranged by
Andrew D. Gordon

RIFF 47

Jazz Blues

CD track 47

Composed & Arranged by
Andrew D. Gordon

RIFF 48

Gospel Blues

CD track 48

Composed & Arranged by
Andrew D. Gordon

RIFF 49

Funky Blues

♩ = 120

Composed & Arranged by
Andrew D. Gordon

RIFF 50

Hip-Hop Jazz Blues

Composed & Arranged by
Andrew D. Gordon

CD track 50

RIFF 51

Hip-Hop Jazz Blues

CD track 51

Composed & Arranged by
Andrew D. Gordon

Learning The Basics Of Blues Improvisation
Basic 12 Bar Blues Progression

CD track 52

The above example shows the chord progression of a basic 12 Bar Blues pattern using major chords. This example is in the key of "C" and consists of the I chord (C), the IV chord (F) and the V chord (G). This 12 measure pattern repeats itself throughout the song. Make sure you count four beats per measure practicing this progression until it is memorised. Once you have mastered the progression in this key try the progression in other keys such as: F, G, A, Bb etc. In the key of "F" for instance the I chord would be (F), the IV chord would be (Bb) and the V chord would be (C). Generally the Blues uses dominant seventh chords instead of major chords. Please go to the next example for the pattern using the dominant seventh chords.

12 Bar Blues Progression utilising 7th. Chords

CD track 53

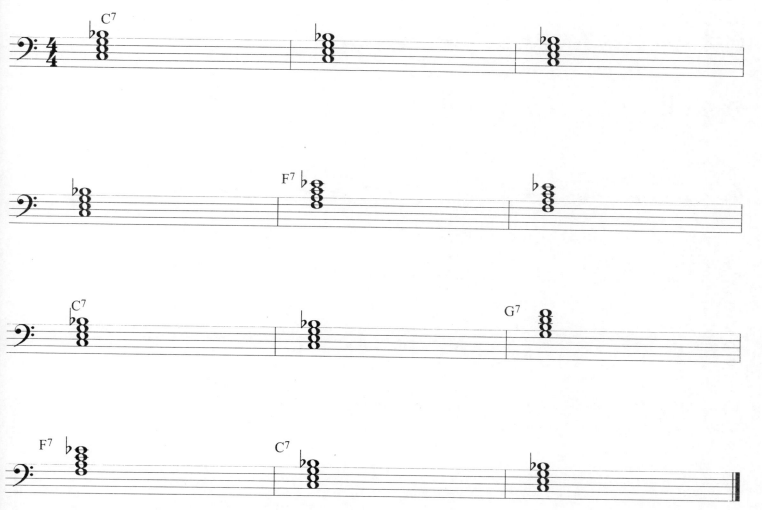

After memorising the previous page, it is now time to add the dominant seventh note to the major chord as shown above. Once again practice the chord progression until it is memorised. The dominant seventh chord is the chord used in the majority of Blues songs. Once this progression is memorised and is comfortable to play at different tempos and as in the first example, different keys, it will be time to add a Blues melody to the 12 Bar Blues progression using the blues scale.

The Blues scale is made up of the following notes of the major scale:

I - bIII - IV - #IV - V - bVII - VIII

In the key of "C"   C   Eb   F   F#   G   Bb   C

By playing notes in the Blues scale along with the dominant 7th. chords you will start to develop the Blues sound as seen in the next example.

Simple Blues Melody Using The Blues Scale

CD track 54

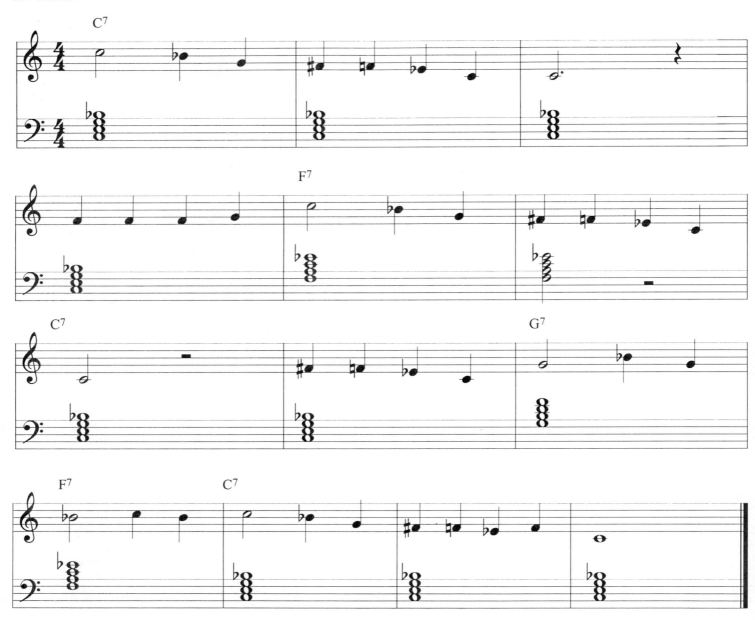

In this example the melody is made up of notes in the "C" Blues scale. The notes of the "C" Blues scale are used throughout the piece even though the chords are changing from C7 to F7 and G7. From this example start creating your own Blues melodies using the Blues scale. You should be able to come up with an infinite amount of possibilities using these notes. The rhythm of the music so far is somewhat basic with the left hand playing whole notes while the right hand is generally playing quarter and half notes. The next example will deal with the rhythmical side of playing the Blues.

Rhythm Pattern For Left Hand Blues Playing

CD track 55

This example shows how to play the left hand chords with more of a rhythmic feel than the previous examples. Once again practice counting this rhythm until it becomes second nature to you. Notice, in measure two, that we have gone to the IV chord (F7), this is a slight variation on the basic Blues pattern of the previous examples and can be used just as effectively.

The next example shows how to add a more complicated melody line, still using the Blues scale, with this left hand rhythm.

Eighth Note Melodic & Rhythmic Blues Progression

CD track 56

This example is now starting to sound more professional in its approach to the Blues. The left hand is the same as the previous example while the right hand is playing eighth note melodic lines using the Blues scale. It is very important to count out the rhythm of the right hand, slowly at first, so that when you finally put both hands together there is little difficulty with the rhythm. I have shown the count for the first line of the piece and you should be able to count out the rest of it. Once again, try making up your own Blues melodies as well as playing it in different keys. Triplet, or Swing rhythm as it is normally called, is another form of rhythm used extensively in both Blues & Jazz and the next examples show how the left and right hands produce this swing rhythm.

Triplet Or Swing Rhythm For The Left Hand

CD track 57

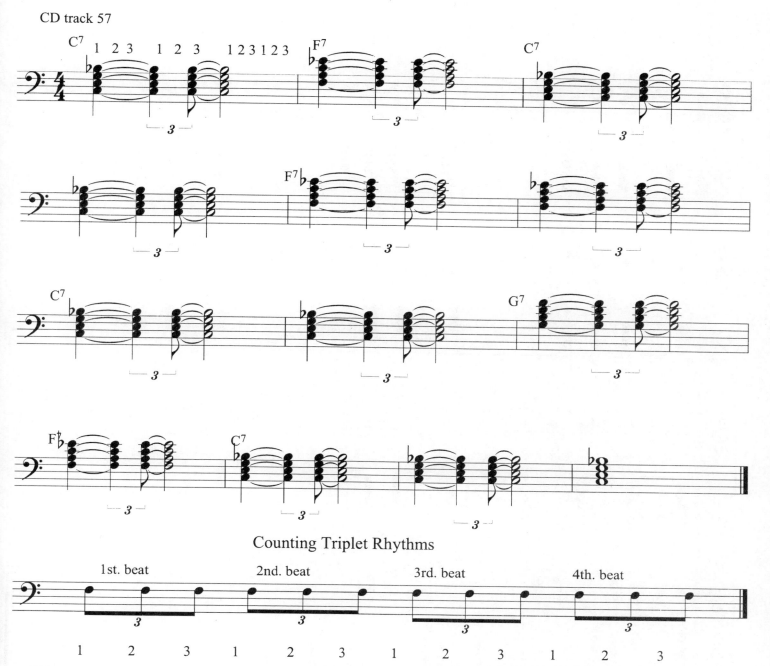

Counting Triplet Rhythms

This example shows how to play and count triplet rhythms as played extensively in Blues & Jazz. Each beat is sub-divided into three, eighth notes producing the triplet rhythm giving the swing feel that has come to be associated with the aforementioned styles. Counting 1-2-3 for each beat is very important to get you started playing this rhythm. Make sure each count is even, as some students have a habit of counting 1-2-3 leaving a pause at the end of the third beat and continuing on. There should obviously be no pause as this would add extra time to the rhythm. The rhythm for the left hand consists of a quarter note tied to a quarter note triplet, followed by an eighth note triplet tied to a half note. The first measure gives an indication of how to count this rhythm. In the next example we will add a triplet or swing rhythm to the melody.

Triplet or Swing Rhythm For Melody and Accompaniment

CD track 58

This example shows how to count and play triplet rhythms with both hands. Once again, the Blues scale is used for the melody. Always try playing in different keys so that you become familiar with the Blues scale and the chord progression in as many keys as possible.

Using Notes Of The Major Scale As Well As The Blues Scale

CD track 59

The Blues scale can, after a while, sound repetitive so this example shows how to incorporate the major scale along with the Blues scale to produce improvised melodic lines. The left hand is playing a typical Boogie Woogie Blues pattern.

By now you should have a reasonable background of the basics of Blues improvisation. By utilizing this section of the book as well as all the 12 bar Blues patterns throughout the book, your Blues piano/keyboard playing should improve in ways that you may not have thought possible!

JAM-A-LONG 1

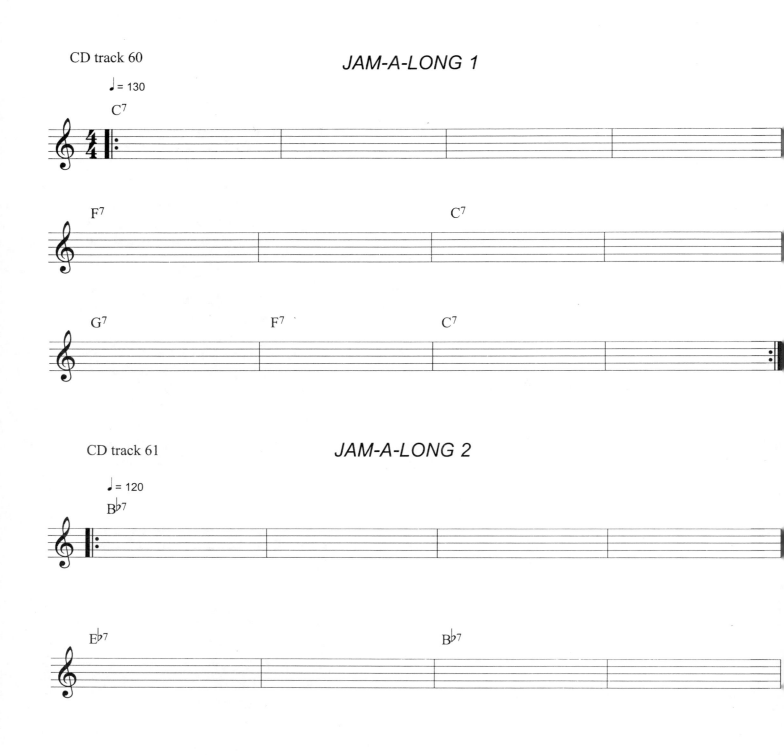

JAM-A-LONG 2

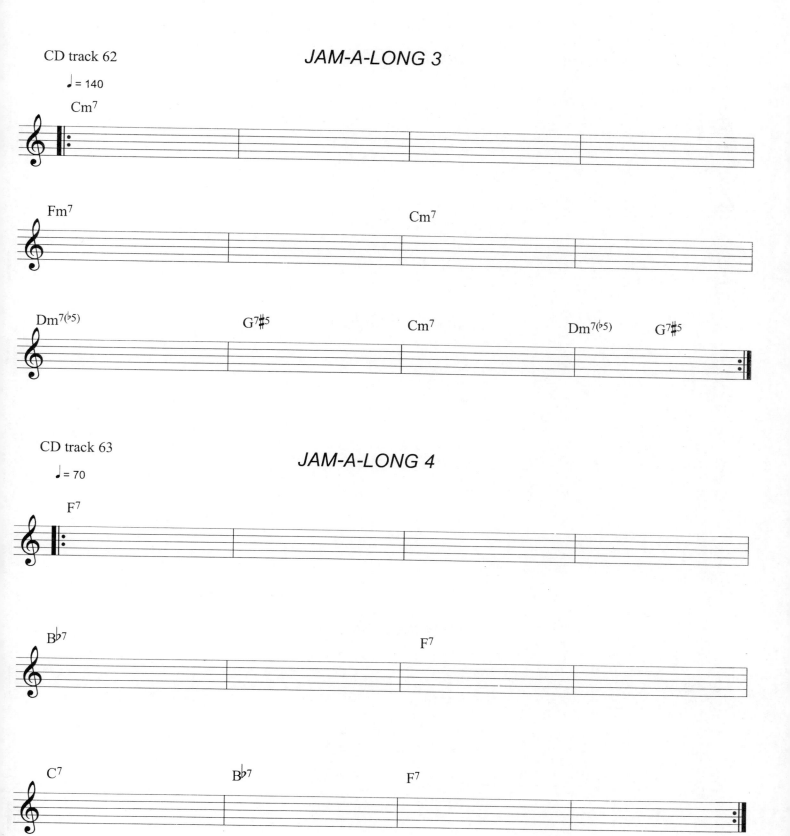